A MILLION REASONS
LIES AND EXCUSES

A MILLION REASONS LIES AND EXCUSES

BRITTANY PRIORE

Disclaimer: This book touches on sensitive topics such as depression,
anxiety, panic, agoraphobia, hopelessness, and sex.

ISBN: 978-0-578-66935-9

Editor: Chelsea Davis
Designer: Tree Abraham

FIRST EDITION

A Million Reasons, Lies, and Excuses may be purchased for
educational, business, or sales promotional use at quantity discounts.
For information, please inquire through www.brittanypriore.com.

For those who loved me through it *all*.

My Little Darlings,

What a magical, tragical, kaleidoscope of emotions this past year has encapsulated me in. I look around and feel content, fulfilled, happy, and most importantly loved – not only by my supportive friends and family but by myself.

It seems natural to love yourself, doesn't it? To accept all that you are and who you are – happy moments and not so happy moments, moments you're proud of, and moments you wish you could do-over.

It's a beautiful thing to be able to look back and recognize those string of moments. To put your ego aside and allow yourself to be vulnerable to growth. This past year has been exactly that – moments of growth. All of which has led me to the woman I am now, the woman I have fought and worked hard to become. I am proud of who I used to be because, without her, I wouldn't be unwavering in who I am today.

The mistakes I've made, the moments of unhappiness I've experienced, the fear I've felt, the isolated veil I've been stuck in don't define who I am, and they certainly don't prevent me from being who I want to be. Just as your mistakes, moments of unhappiness, fear, and isolation don't define you or prevent you from being the best version of yourself.

Depression and anxiety have an artful way of making the world seem grim, but I promise, if you start believing in yourself, setting boundaries, and pushing past your fears, happiness will become a reality, not just a dream. These days I find my world is filled with vibrant pastels that shimmer with each confident step I take, and I am wholeheartedly grateful for that.

This book no longer belongs to me. These words, they're yours. Treat them kindly. Be patient with them. Look past their surface and dive deep into their depth. Sit with them when you feel lonely – just as I did. And, just as I did, I hope you find comfort in them. Because, through it all, you are not now and never will be alone.

With each turning page, I am forever beside you and with you through it all.

Brittany xx

My cloak is red and my flames are deadly
but I'm not the devil you think that I am.

CONTENTS

The Awakening

He was everything to me the moment his tongue outlined my name. I would have chosen not to breathe if it wasn't the oxygen he exhaled. I drank his tears and smoked his breath. I craved his tongue and wrapped myself in his skin.

Holding him didn't satisfy the depths of my needs. I put myself inside of him and made him my home. Because he was home. He was my courage and I his wisdom.

We were one. I was no longer his and he mine. We were we. Spiritually, mentally, physically – we represented the darkest parts of one another, the shallowest graves, and the deepest scars.

Sharing secrets lasted hours and lying in bed lasted days. Consumed with jealousy and addicted to my possession, I cared for nothing else, no one else but him.

He whispers, I will drown in the deepest blues, roar in the fiercest reds, suffocate in celestial black. I will leave a trace of you in every dimension proving love knows no bounds.

He claims to have reaped me. Piece by piece. Stitch by stitch. He alone has painted the colors of my soul; the soft hues of my lips; the deafening brown of my eyes. His fingers have sewn my skin making it a shield, defending me, protecting me from the demons that have haunted me.

He has shaped me. He has given me life. He has shown me love. He is the one I resonate to. The one I call upon. The one I worship. The one I bow down to. He has made me whole for he is the one I put on a necklace to wear around my neck.

He is the almighty, the one who offers unconditional love, the one who has forgiven my sins, and has looked past my flaws.

I feel him beneath my feet and high above the sky. He blinds me, his light – so powerful, so warm, so indulging. I find myself resonating to a higher power, his higher power.

He is everywhere, in everything thing: my father, my mother, my sister, my brother, my friend. Representing the pillars of family and the foundation of friendship.

He is love.

The Seed

April 27th, 1991

I'm here. We're here. *Together.* I'm covered in tears, in laughter, in love, and in hope. Tears for joy, laughter for disbelief, love for gratitude, and hope for the future. But it doesn't last. Those tears dried, your laughter dissipated, your love frozen and left in this moment, and your hope defamed by tragedy.

The Only Love You Knew How To Give

I've held your face in my hands more times than a child should. You have beaten and dragged me across your splintered floor-boards since your womb bled my cries.

You scalped me and used my rooted curls to wash away your turmoil. Ripping off my flesh for shelter, my brain for accolade, my teeth for wit.

I've stood tall through your harrowing storms. Unwavering in your attempts to hector me into submission.

I raise my fists habitually and prepare for bloodshed. Venom falls from your teeth leaving blood on the carpet. All because I am the portrait of a woman you covet to be.

Liability

She sits alone, drinking her tears, and collecting doubt. Swaying back and forth to the rhythmic beat of a panicking heart.

The first time you left...*lines were drawn*

Dear Diary: *The Hours Have Faded into Muted Screams*

I stare out my window and witness the seasons changing. But I'm still here, in the same place. I have not changed, nor have I grown. It's like I'm frozen in time...or lost in it?

I try to silence my mind. I try to suppress my tormenting thoughts. I scream to let go of anger. I cry to let go of fear. I look in the mirror to reassure myself that someone loves me...that someone cares...that someone remembers that I exist.

Invisible Scars

Each time you disappear a piece of me never comes back.

And All of Me Was Plagued With Darkness

It called upon me like it knew me. Begging, pleading for me. Passionately at first, like a forlorn lover. Its malevolence was masked. Presenting itself as relief. Reassuring me it was here to console me; to sit with me in my time of need.

My resistance ignited a rage within it. As I turned to run, it roared. Spewing demons and unleashing hate. I could feel the pull of sadness reeling me in while fear deftly wrapped itself around my throat. *Tell me*, it screamed. With a sinking in my heart and an emptiness in my chest, I surrendered…

I feel alone for reasons I cannot explain, for reasons unknown. It's an emptiness that haunts me, that fills me, suffocating me to my bones. A love within me that does not exist.

A 28-Year Haunting

I waited up for you to come home until my weary eyes
allowed it no more. Night after day, a ghost of you was all
that remained in our home.

10-26 West Park Road

Down winding roads and under tall oak trees up on the
second floor started the beginnings of a new family of three.

Dear Diary: *Fear Has Become My Only Friend*

Looking up into the night sky used to make me feel alive. Looking up into that state of darkness used to empower me and free me from a world of plastic hearts and cold touches. It used to make me believe in so much hope and I've completely let go of that. I've lost touch with love. I can hardly recognize happiness. I no longer know stability. All that surrounds me is fear.

You hurt me in ways I couldn't prepare myself for.

Fear.

Casting a dark shadow over my mind, paralyzing all my senses and destroying my identity.

If I could...

I would take away the memories that ignite your anger. I would hold you in my arms and protect you from the love that you were shown. I would protect you from the past that chases you. A defenseless child lost in the traumas that berated another. I should've done more to protect you. Forgive me, brother.

Please, forgive me.

With each new moon, I fall heavy into defeat.

Family Portraits

The lies cover the shelves in each ceramic fame. They hang on the walls. They're slipped into leather folds. Its beauty is presented at each crossing, and so a thousand words are exchanged, truth not being one of them.

I lost track of daylight having not slept for a hundred years.

The Flower, The Honey, and The Bee

I fall to my knees in solace. Placing my lips on the pads of your divinity. An ethereal love I have been waiting for has finally brought cessation to a civil war that has lasted eighteen years.

The color of kindness. The texture of love. The rough edges of humility. Translucent in your rarity, you open your arms enveloping me in an intimacy I have never believed in.

Your heart is boundless; carrying the past, present, and future it holds the beats of a thousand wo(men). Does my rhythm play a tune more notable than the rest?

I bow my head at your worthiness. You lift me from the shrapnel, lap the debris off my face. I hear the dropping of weapons. I feel the healing of wounds. You untie my wrists and let down my hair. Placing your hand in mine you say, *now it is time for peace.*

My hungry eyes crave to taste you.

He opens his mouth and starts speaking in tongues and suddenly the ground beneath me is burning.

I've covered the mirrors, lining them with empty memories of a broken home.

Baby Blues or Angry Oceans?

The color of your eyes is part of your disguise they paint who you really are. I look into them blindly. Wondering... did I do this to you?

I suppose you never get the story ending you imagined when one child raises another.

And in that moment, in that first kiss...my little darling, I knew you were a wonder of the world.

Blood is thicker than water they say.

It will drown you faster.

The Clock Struck Midnight and The Lies Washed Over Me

One word, false in its meaning becomes two words and then three. Until suddenly, the lies have become my reality, and the world no longer sees *me*.

In the Garden of Daffodils

His warm body beneath my fingers, his stubble brushing against my pink cheeks, his beauty radiating from my brown eyes.

I breathe you in and my legs quiver in anticipation. I'm bathing in puddles of my own lust. Touch me. Reach down and feel the deepest parts of me. Close your eyes. Sleep inside of me and make me your home. Sink into me. Get lost in the mosaic blues of my oceans. Love me and forget all that came before me.

Tomorrow Will Be Different

Mama, can you hear me?
Mama, I'm screaming.
Mama, my voice is cracking.
Please, mama, answer me.
Mama, I love you.
Do you love me?
Mama, I'm trying so hard.
Can you see me?
I'm trying.
I really am trying, mama.
Mama, I'm tired.
My voice is strained.
I can't catch my breath.
Please just answer me, mama.
I am here.
I am still here.
Why am I not enough?
Please, mama, sit with me.
Spend time beside me.
Mama, I promise, if you get to know me,
it will be different between us.
Come, mama, take my hand.
Let me show you my world.
We can start with you.
Tell me what you want, mama.
Is he kind to you?
Do you feel loved?

Because I love you, mama.
Isn't that enough?
Why isn't that enough?
Why am I not enough, mama?
Mama, please.
Mama, my knees hurt.
I've been down here too long.
Mama, please slow down.
Don't walk away.
Please, mama.
Please.
Mama?

I'm jealous of any woman who has touched you,
who has danced in your shadows, who has been
betwixt by your gaze.

You are mine.
Carve it into your tongue and repeat it to me.

You are mine.

I know her promises are covered in lies
but her lies are covered in hope.

Paean.

*The flex and rise of my hips as he makes his way from nape
to navel.*

Dear Diary: *In an Effort to Avoid Him, She Avoided Us Too*

Her absence still leaves me feeling empty. No matter the friends that surround me or the lover in my bed, I'm unable to fill the pieces of me that weren't good enough for her.

You dare not stare into the eyes of a monster. She crushes the innocent with her insecurity and doubt. Jealousy roars from her lips, hatred drips from her eyes, and happiness...is lost on her.

If you see her...*run.*

You've been warned.

Through gritted teeth and blistered knees, I begged her,
please stay.

Dear Diary: *His Shadow Keeps Me Warm*

He has a transformative heart that shines throughout him. Strangers fall in awe upon meeting him. His calming spirit instantly cuts through the polite and ordinary. An angel I tell him. You're an angel walking, breathing amongst us. I say, long after you're gone, what a blessing it will be to have you shining down on us all.

I know...you're thinking I build motes around him simply because I love him. But that's not the truth. I speak of his kindness as if I am blessed to have been embraced by it. I speak of his patience as something foreign to have come by. He is a rarity. What else do you expect me to do with such a thing but cherish it?

When the War Paint Comes Off

I laid down my weapons
and showed you my scars.
Yet, you still insisted on war.
I fought with love and compassion
and you fought with your fists.

You took what you needed
and walked away.
Never turning around
to see me lifeless on the floor.

Fix me, I cried.
Love me, I begged.
Don't walk away, I pleaded.
Take away the pain, I insisted.
Give me back my life, I screamed.

You never turned around.

Why me?
When there's three?

My delicious little lover...oh, how I cherish you.

Like children, we laugh, and we play, and we scheme, and we say forever. We make promises with no intention of breaking them.

Like children, when the sun goes down, our day fades behind us, and when we wake the next morning, the excitement of yesterday has lost its magic.

Even angels wear red sometimes.

With Daffodils Beneath Our Feet

I ripped my heart out and handed it to you. You cracked your rib and offered it to me in return. And, there we stood, a heartless woman and a man one rib short of understanding.

Lullabies

She screams my name, and I'm trapped by her words, wrapped up in her lies. And, so I lay in the sound day after night.

He tells me I'm his black beauty, his black dahlia, his most serene nightmare come to angelic form; his worst demons turned celestial. I tell him I'm done being someone's muse. I want to be someone's North Star, their refuge on route to sanctuary.

Dear Diary: *The Funeral Is in Site*

It's in his empty messages and short goodbyes…so I dress myself in black and stray from the light. I get down on bended knees and pray, asking for a love that will stay, asking why I'm not ever enough.

Many thought it was he who fell too quickly. But it was I who crashed.

When day turns to night, I turn to pray, and you turn over.

Lover, I've worn out the floor waiting for you to come home...

I would capture
your shadows
lasso your ghosts

All to keep
even the most
foreign parts
of you

close to me

I am still wondering hopelessly in the same place he left me. Without vision and without intent and that reality doesn't parallel his escape. Don't you see? He has seen the world and I have merely traveled the same backroads for 18 years. My destination isn't written in the stars. It's shackled to the street signs and lamp posts that line my block.

The Unraveling

"You love the world more than you love yourself, and, my darling girl, I cannot watch you live like that anymore."

He turns to leave, and I fall to my knees
begging for absolution.

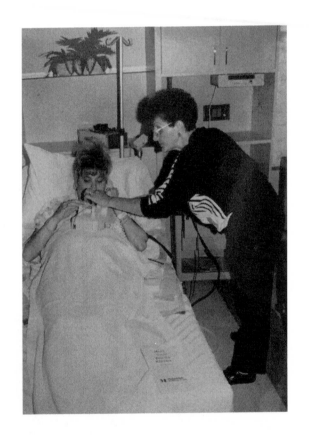

The bruises on my knees, the lacerations on my back, they were put there long before my conception.

September 6th, 2010

The smell of the wet pavement,
the sounds of flickering streetlights.

I remember it all.

The time – 11:47 pm.
The day – September 6th, 2010.

I remember it all.

The look on your face.
A rueful smile
and a sigh of relief.

I remember it all.

The feelings – empty, confused, broken.
The realism of my nightmares.
The fantasy of my dreams.

I remember it all.

Do you?

The Ghost That Haunts Me

I step forward,
grabbing his face in my hands.

I love you.

Memorizing the creases around his eyes,
the stubble on his chin.
I trace my thumb over his lips.

I love you.

I make a mental note
to remember that
his right iris has a freckle.

I love you.

One moment it's here
and it all seems so secure
and permanent.
and forever
and strong.

And, then, suddenly
it's not.

It's broken
and fragile
and temporary.

And, then,
it's gone.

Don't forget me.

It sounded like
a regretful
and maybe even a
desperate goodbye.
But it wasn't.
It was a true testament:

Don't forget me.

In which hour, during which day...*in which moment*, my love, did you start unloving me?

Your laugh still bellows in my stomach. Your pain strikes my heart leaving me breathless for days. Remnants of your smile can be found in the creases of my laugh. Your tears stain my cheeks, marking me for eternity. And what am I to you but a dream you have forgotten once the morning light kisses your eyes?

I can't exist in a world where your love for me doesn't.

My darling, you left me. You left me without saying goodbye. Without saying goodbye to us and our time together.

My darling, I'm losing all sense of sanity. I see your face in every crowded hallway. I save a seat for you at every table. I wait up for you every night.

My darling, I don't remember a time when my thoughts weren't clouded by judgment and preconceived anger. I don't trust myself anymore.

My darling, I'm standing here confused, cursing at the moon. Counting the stars and comparing their beauty to our love, daring the sun to rise on such a sardonic night.

My darling, I don't know who I am without you. I look in the mirror only to see your reflection staring back at me.

My darling, do you love me? Because I love you. Do you miss me? Because I miss you. Do you hear me? Because your laugh still echoes in my head.

My darling what an undeserving affection you possess of me.

My lover, look at what you've done to me...
loving you has destroyed me.

Black Beauty

You will search for me in every woman you make love to. You will hear my voice in every song she sings. You will taste me on every tongue you caress. Falling in love with me was easy. Forgetting me will be the hardest thing you will ever do.

You are only but my heart, not my soul.

I can live without you.

The Stem

It was mid-day when he called, *"I can't tell you how many times my mind has wandered to you."*

This probably won't make much of a difference, but I'll repeat it as many times as necessary. I am sorry for what I said and the way I made you feel. You don't deserve to feel that way, nobody does. Please try to understand. I am sorry. I love you.

You were right in all that you said. I can't take back the way I have made you feel for the past several months, eventhough I wish I could. Thank you for loving me so deeply. I hope to one day be able to do the same for you.

I love you with all my heart,

Richard

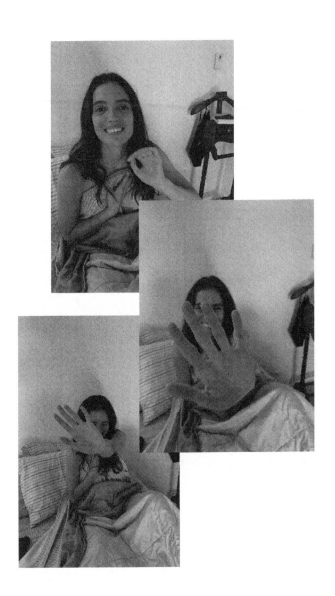

Through daffodil colored lenses the ugliness that I see in myself is lost on you.

He was the first who didn't see my flaws as
something that marked me *hopeless.*

Each tender moment his lips grazed my neck brought me closer to myself.

You wrapped me in daffodil chains, dragged me across the rough edges of humility, through the harrowing storms of self-doubt, and over the fields of forgiveness. When we arrived, you filled my cracks with gold and drew hearts around my bruises. Through my reflection in your eyes, I saw myself, I saw the truth.

You Introduced Me to Myself

In secret gardens and hidden valleys, in forgotten corners and dead-end roads, I found pieces of me in parts of you.

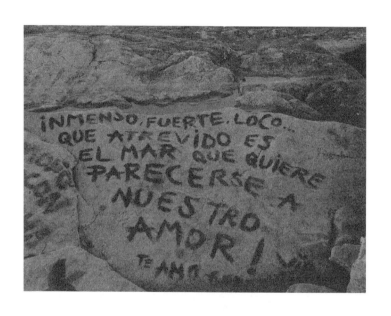

It's a love so intimate and tender and unraveling. It leaves you powerless in its wake.

Dear Diary: *I Can't Find My Way Out*

I've never suffered from self-doubt or perhaps I never recognized it in myself until now. I have always found jealousy a waste of emotion — one that spreads and cripples the mind like a baneful disease. But, now, when I look in the mirror, that's all I see. A girl drowning in self-doubt and choking on jealousy. I'm lost and I keep running for help, but it is only when I run back to myself that I realize I am stammering around in circles.

From Her, To You, To Me

I'm used to the betrayal. I was born with knives sticking out of my back.

Will you leave me like she did?
Will you find someone who fills you in ways I can't?
Am I enough for you?
Do you see a future with me in it?
Will you forget me like she does when he walks in?
You say you're not the same person.
Can you promise me that?

Dear Diary: *Today is July 15th, 2014*

It has only been my father to demonstrate such love. To handle me gently and without reservation… to love me without restriction. It's something I never thought could be found outside the confinements of my home, outside the safety parameter my father has built in my defense. But as I look now, I see my home has expanded, and not by measure, but by vessel.

02-14-14

Dear Daffodil;

Happy Anniversary My little flower!
The past three years of My life
with you have been something
unforgettable. I am so happy to
have you by My side and I would
not want it any other way.
You are My best friend and My lover.

You are silly and beautiful with a
bigger heart than anyone I know.
I love being with you, even when
it is just sleeping in the same bed.
I can't picture My life without you.

I love you so much

Universally Kindred

Sheltered from harsh realities, not knowing his defenses, he fell into me. We crashed and burned but as we burned, we soared. Higher and higher we did not plummet. Instead, we rose grander than any force.

Through the muted pastels
I've painted in defense.

They see me.

Through the fog
I've been floating in.

They see me.

Through the deception and lies
Encrypted on my skin.

They see me.

So, deeper into the ground I burrow,
The more masks I paint, and the louder I speak.

Somewhere in the back of my mind, I knew you were here...
dancing along the shore, looking up at the moon, sitting under
the stars. I knew you were here...*somewhere waiting for me.*

Am I beautiful?
You're beautiful.

Say I it like you mean it.
You're beautiful.

Say it again.
You're beautiful.

Eulogize it, say it so I believe it.
Only you can do that.

I give and give as to not appear lonely or broken.
Knowing if they left, in their absence, I would be
happier and remain just as whole.

Trade hearts with me sister, *I can make you better.*

Lay Out Your Palm and I Will Come Willingly

My loyalty is dedicated to you, my love. Each night, I bow my head and ask God to make you happy, I beg him to keep you safe. The golden bricks beneath your feet…I have placed them there. The bed in which you lay upon is made of my tendrils and talon. You see, my love, I'd do anything for you. I've searched the dimensions, scoured the ocean floors, traveled lifetimes all in search of a love like yours. I would do anything for you. Without expectation, I would meet your every desire. I have chosen to give you my body, to trust you with the safekeeping of *my* soul. All I ask in return, my love, is not for the same hand-carved gestures. I simply ask you to love me without possession, to allow me to keep my freedom. I love you, but I don't need to own you. Keep your freedom and I'll keep mine. When my head rests upon your pillow, know I'm there of my own volition.

România

Go back eighteen years, watch the reaping and sewing of celestial events, and you will find we were molded from the same stars.

In the darkest times, her voice has shown me light. At the highest peaks, her heart has shown me humility. In striking moments, her joy has shown me love.

I'm complete in your eyes.

I wish I could see myself the same way.

Daffodil,

My time with you has been amazing, I can't put into words how happy I am, you're amazing. All I could ask for...

you are beautiful, understanding, funny, smart ... you're my best friend.

I adore everything about you, your smile, the way you put up a peace sign, the way you break those hand hearts and crush them, the way you laugh.

Thank you for believing in me, you've really helped me grow. Thank you for all that you have given me. Thank you for giving me your heart.

I love you.

P.S.   you have my heart.

Surrounded but always painfully alone.

Beware of the girl with two faces, each side more deceitful than the other.

Why do they bring out the worst in me?
Is it because there is no best of me?

Take me, take me away from here.
Run away, run away with me.
Hold me, hold me tighter.
Love me, love me harder.

A Family Home

I'm trapped inside of a house. Time has slowed down. I'm unsure of how long I've been in here. Day after day, I'm surrounded by these same four walls.

One wall is tall and so brightly colored it's deafening. It tells me I'm a liar, it tells me I'm manipulative, it tells me I'm selfish, it tells me I'm unlovable.

One wall has been overgrown by weeds, hiding its original structure. It tells me I'm a hypocrite, it tells me I'm judgmental, it tells me I'm bad, that I'm no good, that I'm nothing, that I'm nobody.

One wall is short and jagged. It cuts me when I approach it. It tells me I'm vain, it tells me I'm arrogant, it also tells me I'm selfish.

The last wall used to be covered in fire but now it's a block of ice. This wall used to keep me warm but now I shiver standing next to it. This wall is silent. It doesn't speak to me anymore. It has given up on me.

The bright wall is relentless. It is the foundation holding up my insecurities. It pretends to protect me, it kisses my flaws, but points them out to passersby on the sidewalk. It's growing taller and taller each day.

The wall of weeds used to hold so much beauty — it's hard to recognize it anymore. So, I try to cut them down but in turn, it pricks me with its thorns. I tried watering it instead. That only made it raise its thorns higher.

The jagged wall is the most volatile. It uses me. It takes and takes and when I have nothing left to give it tells me I'm a bitch.

The ice wall used to love me. It used to speak kindly to me. It understood me. It saw the good in me. It used to protect me and keep me safe from things like thorns, jagged edges, and bright colors. Now, it listens to their lies. It's starting to believe them. This wall now tells me I'm bad, that I'm nothing.

I tell these walls I'm sorry. I tell them I never meant to do anything wrong. I ask them for forgiveness. I tell them they're better off without me. I ask these walls to set me free. I beg them to let me go. I tell them that if I go, I'll keep running and I'll never come back, that they will never have to deal with me again. But they only laugh and tighten their borders, leaving no room for me to escape.

Dear Diary: *I'm Wicked...But They Are Too*

I'm drawn to the impurities brushed upon another. Their misfortunes are some of my greatest victories…what is wrong with me? Has my own self-hatred washed away my compassion? Has it blinded me from looking past the superficialities that deserve but a second look? I see the beauty, I admire it, but I can't help but celebrate the one thing that flaws them.

You call it *making love.* I call it a *fight* with my body.

Right there, I could've started over, but I did the same shit. I opened my mouth, gossiped, and lied. What else do you expect? I'm my mother's daughter after all.

Dear Diary: *These Questions Leave Me Feeling Empty*

When I look in the mirror, the reflection staring back is hatred in all of its manifestations. I try to count the ways in which I love myself – only to fail each time. I can't even utter the words or imagine trying to. How will anyone ever love me, if I'm unable to love myself? And if I'm unable to love myself, can I ever really embrace love from another? Does anyone really love me? My friends? My family? They don't know me. They don't know the darkness that fills my mind. They can't see through the lies I tell. They only see what I want them to see. They don't really know me, and if they don't really know me, how can they really love me? That question leaves me feeling lonely...even with my lover lying next to me.

And if I die before I wake, I invite you to dance atop my ashes.

I deserve it.

Trust me, I'm as ugly as you say I am.

Vatican City

I don't belong here. Such beauty painted upon these walls, engraved in these stones. I'm far too ugly to take up the space surrounding such art.

How can you love a monster?
A jagged-tooth, cockeyed monster.

A monster, a lion in sheep's skin is how you see me. You say, despite the love I'm shown, I leave bite wounds on whoever kneads me.

And you're right.

12 Westbourne Grove Terrace

Each step I took was to put distance between who you are and who I don't want to be, yet our destinations parallel.

If you look in the mirror long enough, you'll see your mistakes etched across the surface of your skin.

Why isn't love enough?

I've asked God, I've begged him:

Give me her disease, God.
Infect me with her addiction.
I can handle it, God.
She's not strong enough, God.
I am. I am, God.
Please give it to me, I beg you.
I will fight it for both of us, God.
I am stronger than she is, God, please.
She's suffered too long.
I want her to be happy, God.
She deserves to be happy.
Don't you think she deserves to be happy, God?
God, please. Help me help her.
Rid her of this disease, God.
She's been down there too long.
Give it to me, please.
She deserves more.
Give her more and give me less.
I'm asking for it, God.
I take it willingly.
If it means her happiness, I surrender, God.
God, please.

Dear Diary: *Blue and Green Aren't So Pretty Up Close*

I am sat still, trembling, with bullets of sweat puddling my feet. One thought, a simple seed, blossoms, and grows into a forest. I am blinded and unable to see my way out. I close my eyes and breathe only to open them and see I've drifted farther from the dark green that surrounded me only moments ago. *Help.* I'm screaming, though I fear I'm too far gone to be heard. *Help.* I scream louder. This time someone will hear me, they have to. *Help.* I'm starting to drown. The puddles beneath my feet have turned to vast oceans and I've forgotten how to swim. Help. I've become too tired, too weak to paddle. So, I'll float… even further away.

"Sink or swim," they said. *I chose to drown.*

I'm pacing the floor, licking my wounds, trying to speak to the parts of me that have been ignored by you, by me, by the dynamics our family settled into.

The child in me is screaming. I wake up with her every night. She seeks a stillness I can't offer, a peace I can't find. She clings to me, looking for reassurance. But I have nothing to give. So, I hold her, rocking her back and forth. I kiss her tears and together we fall asleep, wandering into the darkness of our minds, searching for answers once more.

It was a Friday night. She didn't come home after work...again. We were watching the movie Artificial Intelligence. You, my sister, and me. My little brother was in bed. The movie made me miss her so much. All the boy wanted was to spend one last day with his mom. Just like me. He waited thousands of years to see her, to hug her, to smell her, to love her. Just like me. I wished she was there holding me as I watched it. To tell me she loved me just as the boy's mother did. But she wasn't. She rarely was. Did the movie make you miss her too? Did you, Dad? Did you miss her?

I have questions, Dad.

Once the movie ended, I made my way to your room hoping she would be in there. But she wasn't. I knew she wouldn't be, but still, I hoped. I jumped into the bed and laid my head on her pillow wishing she would walk through the door. She didn't and I cried. *I* cried. *I* cried, Dad. Did you? Did you, Dad? Did you ever cry? Did you want to or were you forced to fake a smile for me? For my sister? For my brother?

I have questions, Dad.

That night I went to bed wondering if she missed me – missed me the same way I missed her. Did the scent of my shampoo put knots in her stomach? Was it a constant reminder of my absence? Her perfume did that to me. The smell made me sick. It made me angry. Because I knew she was leaving. Whenever she put her perfume on, I knew she was leaving. And I never knew when I would see her again. Did you grow to hate the scent of her perfume too? Did you want to grab it and throw it against the wall like I did? Did you, Dad? Did you go to bed crying that night, too? Did you ever go to bed crying at night or did you hold it in? Did you wait until you showered each night like I did? Did you, Dad? Did you ever cry in the shower too?

I have questions, Dad.

I prayed that night. I prayed that things would be better in the morning. That she would wake up and decide to stay. That she would love us the same way that she used to – when she stayed home and watched movies with us on Friday nights, when she was there to hold me when I was sad, when her side of the bed was never empty. Did you go to bed praying that night, Dad? Did you pray too? Did you ever pray for her to love us again like I did? Did you, Dad? Did you pray? Were you disappointed in the morning when she wasn't there for breakfast? Because *I* was. *I* was, Dad. Were you?

I have questions, Dad.

A Decade Has Passed and I Still Feel the Same...

It's time. It slips through your fingers, chisels away at your memories, and has a grim way of making you feel lonely.

Depression is selfish, it likes to keep you to itself. It paints the world in shades of gray in an attempt to keep you blind. You become self-absorbed and begin to lack self-awareness. You become hypersensitive to your own emotions which causes you to forget about everyone else's. The thoughts in your head will become obsessive. You will lose grip on reality as days begin to harmonize to the same despondent tune. Soon, you will fear leaving your house. So, you'll walk quickly and hang your head low. Friends will disappear because they won't understand. They can't – they're happy. They don't know what it's like to feel alone in a crowded room. To feel confused when looking in the mirror while trying to understand your own reflection. Life as you knew it, is gone. You will eventually begin to hate yourself, and those around you. Because happiness will become a distant memory and those who still possess it will become the enemy. Depression is selfish, it likes to keep you to itself.

Generational Warfare

There's a war inside your heart that has held me
captive long before we met. I'm not you and on your
loneliest nights that threatens you...*why?*

On the Bathroom Floor Showered in My Own Tears

Loving you only pushes me further from myself
and I just can't do it anymore.

I'm sorry.

I step into the fire.
Heavenly light, protect me.

I burn in the fire.
Heavenly water, cleanse me.

I dance in the flames.
Heavenly father, join me.

Dear Diary: *I Think I Prefer It Here*

Its company kept me hidden from their judgment. It washed away their concerns and drowned out the echoes of their opinions. Darkness, a place I thought I would never be happy in again, became my solitude once more.

You are blissfully unaware of the scars you left
in the darkest corners of my mind.

I have questions, Mom…why weren't we enough?

Heavenly Father, what good is redemption if I enjoy dancing in the shadows?

Denial

The dam breaks and your water comes
rushing in. It's only when I'm drowning
that I realize *I miss you.*

I've sat in the darkness long enough to recognize the truth
and still…

> *I can't admit it to myself.*

I followed my fears and they lead me to *you.*

That mouth is your most lethal weapon and still,
I long for your lullabies.

Ignorance Is Bliss

Look at me. Look at what you've done to me. Look at how you left me. I'm your daughter. How is it that you ignore my pain with such ease when I once lived and breathed off the beating of your very heart? Please tell me, tell me that you're unaware, that you are too busy dancing in the colors of your newfound freedom. Because I can't accept it. I can't accept that you know of my wounds but refuse to acknowledge them.

Don't you see? Don't you see what you've done to me? I replay broken memories over and over in my mind wondering why it took so long for them to manifest into chains. I surround myself with toxic love because it's the only kind I know, and so the cycle of abuse continues in women who take your shape.

Pride washes over me, choking me until I'm on the brink of reality. I grit my teeth, unable to admit it's you, but it is, *it is you*. You're the root of my weakness and I hate it. Because who are you to me but a woman who loved herself more than the very child she gave life to?

The Ceiling Is Caving In

I lost myself in her empty words, but I will find myself in this desolated peace.

You have become the echo of
a beloved childhood tune I can no longer
remember the words to.

For 27 years, I burned like a witch at the stake with my hands tied. You set my skin ablaze and I let you. Only it was I who lit the match. I turned myself to ash to keep you warm.

The Flower

Your bed of daffodils turned to weeds.

Dear Diary: *He Loves My Deceit, Not Me*

Each night, he lies down with love in his heart and hope for our future. And I lay down questioning my existence. Wishing to wake up prettier, smarter, wittier. I hate myself. I hate myself. I hate myself. I hate myself. I wish I could say it out loud. Admit it to myself loudly. To scream it. But I can't. Because it will wake him up. But I do. I hate myself. I hate everything about me. I hate the control I harbor inside. I hate the fear rushing through me. I hate the thoughts in my head. I'm not who they think I am. They don't know me. He doesn't know me. If he doesn't know me, how can I be with him? He's loving a lie. He's fallen in love with a version of me that doesn't exist. He's planning a future with a version of me that doesn't exist. If he finds out the truth will he leave me? Of course, he won't. That's not my boy. He will love me harder and kinder and that will only suffocate me and make me feel unworthy and weak.

We are *never* alone in a crowded room.

I see everyone but I don't see you.

We look so happy. But it was all a lie because I wasn't.

The Lies We Tell Ourselves

We've ripped out a few pages from our love story. Best not to catch that second hand when so many hours hold so many untold truths.

Wicked Lovers

It is merciful for a saint to love a sinner, yet blasphemy for a sinner to love a saint, and so I wonder if our unholy union will prosper through the ages.

You're lucky to have found him.
You're lucky to be with him.
You're lucky to know him.

...isn't he lucky too?

Some days he is my heaven.
Some days he is my hell.

It's curious, isn't it? How one day a perfect stranger can become home and home can go on to become four battered walls and a leaky roof.

*I wonder…*is it that you see *me*, or are you painfully blinded by love and simply unable to see *me?*

Dear Diary: *It's A Different Rabbit Hole Every Day*

Today, I wake up with a thought that differs from yesterday. Yesterday, I was fearful of my future, my capabilities, my talent. My anxiety told me I would never be successful. I would never love. My life would be empty – that it would resemble the silhouette of a woman that, in theory, and by illusion, had it all, but in the grim reality of her own mind, was empty. A pacing heart that never settled; therefore, pushing everyone away.

My anxiety told me my lover would tire of this routine and move on to another. One thought leads to another that leads to another that eventually leads me to believe they are right. He will leave. I will be alone. I will never be capable of loving purely.

But that was yesterday. Today, my anxiety tells me I'm unhappy. It tells me to leave my lover and move back home. To run away and never look back. I don't want to believe this. Just a few short weeks ago I was happy in our home. Planning for the holidays, hanging pictures, and lying in bed on Sunday mornings.

Today, it tells me I was wrong, and these 9 years have wasted my life. I fight them. I ask them to stop. I tell them to leave me and my lover alone. That we're happy despite what they say. But they persist. Guilt rises. Panic grips. Tears swell. My stomach churns. My limbs go numb. And here we are again. Another night fighting my own mind. Begging for it to leave me in peace. Instead, it leaves me in the midst of a war.

I can't wait for tomorrow. At least those thoughts will lead me further away from the lies of today.

Dear Love of My life:

I can't express to you how much I love you. I am so grateful to be able to call you mine. These years we have spent together have been the best years of my life, because of you.

I miss you when you're not around. Everything makes me think of you. You are the bestest, most beautiful Girlfriend!

Love,
Poffin

I got off my knees only for you to find me with my face down in the pillows.

Run
run away
and free yourself
from the chains that bind me.

Dear Diary: *It's A Lonely World to Live In*

My mind torments me, holding me hostage to my own cruelty. I'm unable to see anything but myself, I'm unable to focus on anyone but myself. The world has become a stranger to me. My lover – how detached he must feel. Sitting side by side, but realities apart.

I look over at him and wonder how it must feel to be surrounded by such peace, to have such control, to be so strong. The thought leaves me feeling even lonelier. He speaks but I'm unable to hear him. He holds me but I'm unable to feel him. I only hear myself – the illogical abuse of my own thoughts.

I reach for him, screaming for peace. I beg him to break the barriers of my mind. Join me. Please, my love, I beg. I can't be alone in here much longer. I need someone to understand it, to see what I'm going through.

But he can't. No one can. Nor would I ever want them to.

Please don't look at me.
I don't want you to remember me this way.

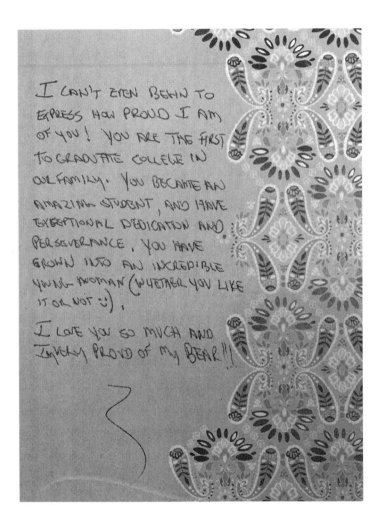

I CAN'T EVEN BEGIN TO
EXPRESS HOW PROUD I AM
OF YOU! YOU ARE THE FIRST
TO GRADUATE COLLEGE IN
OUR FAMILY. YOU BECAME AN
AMAZING STUDENT, AND HAVE
EXCEPTIONAL DEDICATION AND
PERSEVERANCE. YOU HAVE
GROWN INTO AN INCREDIBLE
YOUNG WOMAN (WHETHER YOU LIKE
IT OR NOT :)).

I LOVE YOU SO MUCH AND
I'M VERY PROUD OF MY BEAR!!!

I've become a grim reality and hopeless dream...
how disappointed you must be.

I'm sorry, dad.

How it must have felt to love someone more
than they were capable of loving themselves.

Life after life
you will be mine
and I will be yours.
Me your poison
and you my cure.

Life after life
you will be too good for me
and my deprecation will
bring you to your knees.

Life after life
I will cast doubt.
You will shine love
and every time you walk away
you will wonder why you weren't enough.

Life after life
I'll throw hand grenades
fueled by bitterness and sorrow.
With cracked ribs and bruised knuckles
you will fight for a better tomorrow.

Life after life
I'll push you away
and you will wrap yourself around me
and beg me to stay.

I've fallen down *again* and I don't think
you have what it takes to save me this time.

Dad, if my hero has lost his power
what hope do I have?

Dear Diary: *I Don't Want To Die But I Don't Want To Live*

I look down and I see him happy. He's happy with someone who loves him in all the ways he should feel love. She speaks his native tongue and when he looks at her, he's looking at her – not one of the many masks she paints in lies, lies she uses as a disguise that keeps him from seeing who she really is.

His worry is at ease. He's at ease because he's not worried about me. He's found peace. He finds peace in the pitter-patter that echoes from the floors as he walks through the door after work.

It's a glum feeling, to see him living his life without me — inside jokes I will never understand, an intimacy I will never be a part of, a laugher I will never hear, a stillness I will never cause.

Even so, I want him to take his time, to enjoy his life, to make up for the 10 years he wasted on me. I'll be waiting for him. Just as he was always waiting for me – waiting for my sun to rise, my clouds to pass, my torrents to ease. Because if he's happier without me then I can find a way to be happy for him.

"There are some paths we must walk alone, but I will always be here. Do you hear me?" He grabs my shoulders. "Look at me," he screams.

"I will not leave you. Do you hear me?" Tears fill his eyes. "If you go astray, I will follow you — no matter how dark the path."

Such power in his voice, such promise. But I don't hear him. Not really. There are words and there is sound. But there is also silence.

"If you get lost, reach for me. I am here. I will always be here to help you find your way out." He pulls me to his chest. "You are not alone."

But I am alone — in his embrace, in my head, in our bed at night.

Who I Am To You

I don't recognize the person you have turned me into, the person I've allowed myself to become. I've done nothing but blame you for every insecurity, for all the bloodshed, for the war we started but refused to end.

When I was *just* as much to blame.

Keep us alive in my darkest hour.

He laid beside me, collecting my tears,
recounting their purpose:

Each one that falls will bring you a brighter day.
Imagine the beauty that is ahead of you.

— A father's hope

In a bouquet of daffodils, in the sweet cinnamon of
Horchata, in the melody of our favorite lullabies is
where you will always find me.

Soulmates

It will never wash away
under the deep blue sea.
Years beyond our ending
lives, our love will remain
in the new blue sky.

I wonder…how it must have felt to find me on the floor asking God to take my life.

My Father's Embrace

It's a place of innocence, a place that protects
me from new-aged monsters that hide under
my bed.

I Understand Now

There are holes in your heart only a mother and father can fix. We're all the outcome of our parents' love...or the lack thereof.

You told me you blame the stars for my pain. You say nobody should find solace up there. Velvet blue is beautiful but it's no place for hope. You turned around and told me to find comfort in the wind because it will follow me wherever I go. I shake with each breeze that passes, the shadows are too cold for me, I say. I ask you if pacific blue is better. You remind me I'm afraid of depth. To stick to the shore, tread lightly on the sand and feel it beneath my feet. As it washes away, it will also set me free.

Dear Diary: *I Hate Everything That Makes Me...Me*

When I look in the mirror, I see a monster. I see a broken image of the person I used to be – a person I barely even remember. When was the last time you looked in the mirror and felt beautiful? I can't remember the last time I looked in the mirror at all. I avoid them. They show nothing but the truth. The ugly. The shame. The lack of any worth. I've given up on myself and mirrors remind me of that.

My Lover, My Savior

When my raw flesh covered the floor, you didn't judge me or give notice to the callouses covering my hands. Instead, you took the weight from me and sat down beside me, offering me relief before the storm.

אושר

Your love has given me the strength to let go.
Your love has given me freedom.

You took my hand and danced with me in the dark.

I hope you've found everything you spent your life searching for.

Don't clip my wings.
I promise I will always return to you.
Set me free and let me fly.

My little flower,

What can I say about these last 10
years. We have had our ups and
our downs, our good times and our bad.
Today I write this to you as happy
as I have been in our relationship.
I can truely say that I love you more
than I ever have before. I want to
spend the rest of my life making you
happy. I am so glad we have made
it this far, having grown so close.
Thank you for being the loving person
that you are and the best partner
I could ask for. I love you so much
and I cannot wait for the next 5
years together.

                    I Love You.

"My darling girl, you will always belong to me. I say that without possession, I say that with loyalty. I will always be with you. In this lifetime and in the next."

Her.

Could it be that the almighty rests in us all?
Sweating from our brow, bleeding from our womb?

Acceptance.

As hard as I fought and as much as I cried, I was never going to be enough for you.

It's taken time, but I accept that now.

In a puddle of tears is how I found her. Facedown, tangled up in her own hair. Bruises covered her naked body. Frail bones made up her shell. An ailing woman drenched in hate, enraptured by her own malice. I pull her from the ground – though her knees are too weak to stand. I rest her head on my shoulder and lay her to rest. She grabs my face and winces. Through tear-stained cheeks, she looks up at me and says...*you're back*.

It's 3 a.m. and I'm ready for confession.

Dear Diary: *I'm Coming to The Surface*

The hatred became a part of me. It made up my identity. It's what I saw when I looked in the mirror and it's what I heard when I spoke. I tried hiding this because I was perceived differently by others. They didn't see what I saw. They didn't know the thoughts that filled my mind or the judgment that syncopated with every word I spoke. So, I put on a facade. I wore a second face. I created a second identity to please the people around me because I was ashamed of who I was and what I represented as a person.

Over time, I lost myself. The little things that made me who I was were eventually overshadowed as I became consumed with this alternate reality I lived in. I suppressed my thoughts and emotions so deeply, I started to actually believe I was the person I presented to the world.

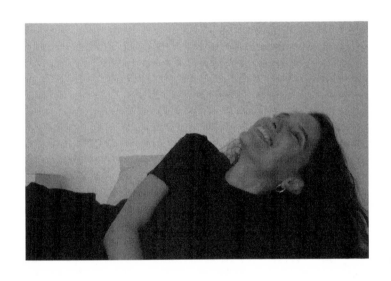

"Sink or swim," they said. *I chose to fly.*

My fingers bleed as I try to turn back the dial. I'm craving the taste of my old tongue, to hear laughter escape the corners of my lips. I don't know how to get back to that life, to that person, to me.

But I'm trying.

Dad,

I think the hardest thing about growing up is the shedding of memories. Day to day, I forget why we're so close even though that bond is what carries me through life. It's only when I sit and flip through photos am I able to recount memories past and what they meant to me then and how they're firmly weaved into who I am now.

I forget about our Friday Family nights – going to Blockbuster and taking our turn to each pick our movie of choice – but always passing on the candy because we had Cajun popcorn at home. I forget about our Tuesday sushi dinner dates that were reserved just for us two. I forget about our days spent at the beach, the cooler of sandwiches you would pack for us even though we always ended up eating $2 pizza slices from Angelo's and 50 cent soft-serve ice-cream cones that were sold from that little blue window on the boardwalk.

I forget about our weekends spent at TY Park. Even though we complained about going you still took us, and I never understood why. Not until I went back as an adult with Olivia and was able to appreciate how that park is able to transport you out of the city. I forget about Sunday mornings – our family chore day – that started with potatoes, eggs, toast, and sausage. I forget how it felt to have you gently wake me up in the mornings before I was met with the sound of alarm clocks. I forget how gentle you were with me when I would fall down and scrape my knee. I forget how it felt to look back and see you waving when I realized you had let go of my bike and I was pedaling on my own.

I forget how it felt driving up to Grandma and Papa's house for the Fourth of July. The parade, festival, and fireworks still bring such fun to the holiday every year even though those traditions are long over. I forget how excited you got for Halloween each year, more so than us kids. I forget about the tenderness in each moment we shared. How your love was so patient and protective.

But I suppose that's the beauty of memories. While they may not be present in our minds every day, the feelings of them are. Because, just as I adored you then, I adore you now, and just as I loved you then, I love you now. Never has a day passed that I questioned your loyalty. I know you will always be by my side. You bring such adventure to every family vacation and holiday. Your excitement for life and the joy you get from making us happy, for making things fun, is why I love you the most. You are selfless and sacrificing while firm and definitive.

In the most colorful parts of my imagination, my childhood dreams live on through the love and patience you continue to give me. Somehow the weight of the world doesn't feel so heavy with you by my side. It would seem as long as I'm "your little girl" there will always remain a part of me that sees the world as inviting and new instead of troubled and complicated. Thank you for keeping me young, thank you for letting me be young. Thank you for being the dad that you are.

I love you,
Bear

Dear Diary: *The Skies Are Clear Today*

I don't know if…I can't say with certainty that I was ever myself – *if that makes sense.* I was the denouement of my childhood and all that it captured. I can't remember a time when I didn't hate the person in the mirror staring back at me. I harbored so much anger, resentment, and fear. I carried myself with those emotions, grew around them, became someone who wasn't capable of living in the daylight. I projected my hostility upon others and sabotaged every good thing in my life. I found myself wanting love, commitment, and security, but upon its arrival, I doubted it and proclaimed it false.

There Are Petals at My Feet and Love in The Air

When the world has turned its back, when the world has created its own imaginative stories, you have held me closer and whispered the truth in my ear.

It wasn't you, but it was you and all that encapsulated what you, as my mother, represented to me. As a child, I created defense mechanisms in an attempt to protect myself from the chaos that erupted daily in our home. Maybe it was something I heard or saw. I can't remember it now.

When I look back, it's almost like a watercolor portrait that has lost its vibrancy over the years. Try as I might, I can't specify which moment it was that I stopped breathing, that I began to hold my breath in anticipation of hostility, that I began to clench my fists in an attempt to protect myself from the ground crumbling each time you left.

I can only attest to who I am now and how those same defense mechanisms have stunted my growth. I've carried them with me into adulthood. Until now, until this very moment, I have carried mechanisms, so deeply suppressed, I have found myself in episodes of debilitating panic since the age of seventeen.

I don't blame you. I never did because I never realized it all led back to you and our broken relationship. Even now I don't blame you. I did this to myself – unintentionally, of course. I can't harbor anger or resentment toward you for something you didn't intentionally do. I know you never meant for this to happen. It simply was the unfortunate outcome of the life you weaved and the choices you made. That's life for each of us – a string of choices and the outcomes that are presented afterward.

I find myself bewildered more than anything else. All these years I questioned the roots. Why do I have anxiety? What causes it? When did it start? How old was I? I may never know those answers. I can only focus on who I am now, and which parts of my younger self need healing.

After all these years, I'm forcing myself to face it all again. I'm going back to reassure the little girl in me who is still crying every night waiting for you to come home. I'm going back to release the anger I felt when you insulted my father in front of me. I'm going back to remind myself it wasn't my fight, my marriage, my divorce to take part in. I'm going back to tell myself that I'm not my father's keeper, he never needed me or asked me for all that I gave up. I did that myself. I'm going back to reflect upon happier memories – because there were happier memories. I'm going back to let it all go. I'm going back today so I can live freely tomorrow.

Dear Diary: *Where Have I Been?*

I fell into a different life. It was as if I woke up one day and the person I had been was gone, and all that was left was a storm of depression, fear, self-loathing, and defeat.

Embers burn my feet as I make my way back to you.

I've been the echoes inside my own head,
tearing myself down, acting as my own enemy.

Dear Diary: *The Truth is Palpable*

It's not because of what anyone else has done or said to me. It's because of what I have done and said to myself. I put myself here.

I was in sixth grade
just walked in
sweaty from the bus

You had fallen asleep
on the couch
with the fuzzy sound
of the TV
in the background

You went shopping
I could tell
because you were wearing
a new gray, slinky shirt
that cut just below your elbows
baby blue track pants
and white and gray Filas

Your arms were folded
at your chest
your pinky resting
on your lips
as it always did
when you would watch TV

I smiled at the site
finding comfort
in knowing you so well
recognizing your habits
and loving how they
make you who
you are

The Parts of Me You Hate

You've mistaken me for your demons because I have become the thing you crave the most: *happiness.*

I would break the back of sanity to save you. I would wrap my tongue around every ruminating thought. I would pack on insecurity once more. I would push myself over the edge, pull myself back up, and do it all over again. I would tie my hands behind my back and fight the world. I would sit cross-legged in rising oceans, drowning in my own fears. I would leave happiness behind if that meant saving you, sister.

Dear Diary: *Who Am I?*

I wish I could rewind the clock. Turn back my life. Slip inside of the old me. But you and I both know I can't. It's impossible to be someone you're not. I was never happy. Those smiles were never genuine, and those laughs only hid my tears. It was a façade, a second face I used to show the world. Somehow, over time, both cheeks began to resemble the same reflection.

I forgive myself.

Parts of Who I Used to Be

When I lost touch with her, I missed her for a short while. Those days are long gone now. Once the lights turned back on and the flooding stopped, I cleaned up the mess she left behind, and I forgot about her.

Learning how to forgive you taught me how to forgive myself.

My Little Darling,

Do you know the ways in which you've changed me and helped me grow? When I first met you, I haplessly didn't have dreams of my own. I simply dreamt of marrying you and raising your little ones while you stood tall in success.

Truthfully, that's where my hopes and dreams for an imaginative future ended. It wasn't until I fell into you that I began to hear my own voice. In the midst of our whirlwind, your dreams never altered for me or the love we shared. Instead, you pursued them fiercely while taking me along with you.

You would never have given up your dreams for me – for us – if our love couldn't co-exist peacefully. You would have chosen to walk away from me. I'm proud of that, of you, of the man you are, of the representation you bestow upon us all.

I used to hate it. I used to find myself angry and almost jealous of your dreams and the passion you had for them – for yourself. It made me feel unworthy and unloved. When it was the purest form of self-love one could ever demonstrate.

You loved yourself and your dreams more than you loved me. That truth was hard to swallow. But I understand now. That's how one should love – for themselves first. The passion you had for yourself forced me to look within and question why I didn't cherish myself similarly. It took years, patience, and formidable lessons to understand how to.

Now, while my love for you has never altered, the love I have for myself has. Thank you for helping me get here.

The Mirror of Your Criticism

I walk and you demand I stand up straight.
So, I lengthen my spine.
Only for you to tell me I am taking up too much space.

I speak and you ask me to heighten my tone.
So, I raise my voice.
Only for you to tell me my opinions are too loud.

I consume and you say it's too much, thighs shouldn't brush.
So, I starve and count my ribs one by one.
Only for you to tell me to widen my arche.

I collect and gather, and you say in modern-day I should hunt.
So, I carve my arrow and prepare to forage.
Only for you to tell me my place is at home.

I Can Never Take That Back

I gave you the best of me, and on some nights...the worst.

Forgive me, please.

Those Empty Memories Haunt Me

In the light of your day, I'm still the darkest version of my worst night. You've depicted me as you knew me, not of who I am or ever truly was.

Loving you still breaks me. Even the pieces of me you've never met.

Dear Diary: *It's A Nightmare I Can't Remember Anymore*

The day I woke up to silence in my head, I knew their judgments were gone. I looked in the mirror and was able to see myself again. The lies etched across my face had disappeared and the scratches from their porcelain smiles had healed. I no longer saw myself in the lies they once told.

I pulled myself from the fiery pits of hell and laid myself under a blanket of stars.

My Sunshine's All Around

I am ready to start dancing in my storms
rather than seeking out shelter from them.

Dear Diary: I'm Not Angry Anymore

I swallowed the pain I allowed her to make me feel – and I say that purposefully. I allowed her to make me feel that way. She didn't make me feel anything. Nobody has that kind of power. The power, or lack thereof, is within us, it's within you, it's within me. I don't blame her for the way I interpreted her cold looks or cruel words. It wouldn't be right to place blame without recognizing my part in our unraveling. Although, I don't blame myself either. We were both hurting. We were both lost. And we both relied on each other far too often for far too much. Friendship – or any relationship for that matter, shouldn't hold so much value. You can't expect one person to give you everything.

Tu Amor Me Cambió

Gracias por todo lo que haces por mí.
No puedes imaginarte lo que tú amor significa para mí.

Why does the fissure between my legs arouse your tyranny?

You allowed me to fall apart, to spill over, to grovel at the break in my back. Not once did you silence my screams, nor did you mute my cries. You gave me room to be vulnerable, to understand myself...to explore myself. You saved me. Simply by being there. *You saved me.*

314

You've witnessed me crumble during my darkest nights. You've held my hand and watched me shine through my brightest days. I am that I am because you loved me.

The Seed

You held me as a child and protected me from the cruelties of the world. You kept me safe and let me run free. You told me I was beautiful and brushed my hair. You painted my room pink and drew my name in the sky. The world is blanketed with your love. I smell it when the wind brushes past gardenias. I hear it in the Landslide that echoes from the radio. And I taste it in golden spoonfuls of Saffron. You surround me despite the miles in distance.

My Body, My Shelter, My Home

They may not be the thickest, to some they may not even be the thinnest, and, to me, they may not be the most well-proportioned. But they're mine and I love them.

The Holy Trinity: Lover, brother, friend.

My Dear Friend, It's Time to Say Goodbye

Drenched in doubt, loathing in insecurity, you wrapped your dirtiest weeds around me. Poisoning my soil and almost causing my extinction. I stand proud to tell you, my new yellow petals have blossomed, and they've grown stronger than the threat of your thorns.

"Heretic!" They yell.

"Self-love!" I roar.

Dear Diary: *They Don't Understand*

Walking away from what hurt me was a conscious and deliberate choice. The act belonged to a deciding factor: who I was and who I am. It became impossible to heal with their judgments and jealousy swarming me. Talking about it only caused them to raise their defenses. In the shallowest and deepest parts of my heart, I understand. It took 27 years for me to look in the mirror and admit the truth. In a lifetime's passing, I only had hate to give. And that hate culminated denial and denial culminated anxiety and anxiety sprouted depression and agoraphobia. I suppressed it all; how I felt and what those feelings eventually did to me – who they turned me into. We're all broken. We're all trying to pick up the pieces with aching backs and racing minds. It's not easy to walk down the road of love. It's easier to sit and stew in hate. Somehow, I found the strength to get up and follow the rising sun instead of continuing to look up at that aching moon. If they can't accept that and respond to who I am now – not who I used to be – then I'm picking up the pieces of me that still need healing and I'm continuing on my journey alone.

I love myself.

Little Brother,

Where do I start? How can I ever tell you how much I love you with bursting into a pile of confetti hearts? You, little boy, changed my life in more ways than you know. I was the baby when you came into our lives, and just a few short years later, this baby grew up quickly only to help raise you.

Most of my life, I resented that, not you, but the dynamic we were placed into. It wasn't fair to you and it certainly wasn't fair to me. I think we made the best of it though. Don't you think? I know there isn't a lot you remember. But, I hope you do remember how much I cared for you, how much I thought of you as more than a brother but not quite like a son – more like an extension of me that needed more dedication and compassion than the other parts of me did.

It wasn't easy to take on such a strenuous mother-type role at such a young age, but I think because of it, we will always be so connected and close. No matter how many days we go without speaking or seeing each other, no matter how many fights we have, no matter the distance, you will always be my little, baby brother whose bright blue eyes made it impossible to say *no* to. Every time you walk through the door, I hear your pitter-patter across the floor. But each time I look up, it's not a baby boy that comes running through the door, it's a young man walking proudly and tall.

That's hard to accept. It so, so hard because I have so many regrets. I was so worried about taking care of you, I always wonder if I was young enough with you? Did we play enough, did I love on you enough? Was I enough for you? As young as I was, I really did try my best.

To this day, I really do try my best. But I need some space. I've needed to stand on my own and be independent of that role for so long. To live my life for me, as a single, young woman living in a world for herself. I hope you understand that and my absence. I need a little time to find myself, to get to know myself, and to only worry about the ways in which I need myself – not the ways in which another needs me or depends on me.

I know it's been quite some time since I've had to physically take care of you, but the emotional aspect of it never goes away. You are always on my mind and weighing heavy on my heart. I hope you know how important you are to me. I am always here for you. I am always your big sister, even if you have grown significantly taller than me.

I hope to see you in London in the next year, but if I don't, please remember this: You are loved. You are enough. You are capable. You are worthy. You, and all that you are, is exactly what the world needs. Without you, life would not be the same.

You gave up your youth
so, I could enjoy mine.

I will never forget that.

Learning how to love you taught me how to love myself.

The Stem

The hatred that once radiated from my skin could burn
down a forest. Now, the love that illuminates could end wars.

I forgive you.

And in that moment, I was...*free.*

I Won't Back Down

Sir, why do you have so much trouble with a woman who doesn't hate herself?

Without love, what is any of this?

I have your brown eyes. I see you every time I look in the mirror. I used to resent them, but now I find comfort in their familiar stare.

A piece of you is always with me, no matter the distance between us.

We share the same experiences, but we are different outcomes.

To all the women who have raised me, my God I thank you.

My Dearest Sister,

I have lived in a very different world than the one that surrounds you. Just as you have lived in a very different world
than the one that captures me. For me, the traumas of our
childhood took precedent by showing up as anxiety and
depression, and, for most of my life, I have struggled with that.
Whereas, for you, they showed up as addiction and, because of
that, most of your life has been a battle.

It's easy for people to judge you because they don't understand, and they probably never will. I try to find peace in that
kind of ignorance by feeling happy for them instead of anger.
Happiness because they have never known such pain, they have
never experienced such dark and undeserving torment that
they faltered or became dependent on something in its promise
to bring them happiness.

However, as someone who could easily have taken the same
route, I get that. I understand your battle and fight for a better
life. Because just as I fight every day for happiness, you fight
every day for sobriety.

Blessed it be the love that held my hand in the dark.
Blessed it be the love that sat in rising waters.
Blessed it be the love that stood tall in my storms.
Blessed it be the love that walked blindly.
Blessed it be the love that believed in me.
Blessed it be the love that saw the truth.

Blessed it be the love that stayed.

I am not just
a daughter,
a sister,
a lover.

I am a woman.

With my own voice
and mind.

Don't worry about me.

I don't need
any version
of a man
to exist.

I am a woman

Father,

You handed me a match
to light the eternal flames
of my own pyre.

From my ashes,
I rose, starting a revolution,
as you said I would.

At times I speak too much. Most of the time I speak too loudly. I have opinions differing from your own, though on the rare occasion we find agreement in our outlooks. I'm passionate and unwavering in my beliefs even with the doubt that encapsulates me. One moment I fear the outcome of my own actions while the next I'm cycling through the desire that comes with each new step. One day I'm enraged with independence while the next I'm craving intimacy and the touch of his hands. My complexity shouldn't ignite a rage within you. It should be a fount for celebration. The more reflections a woman has, the better.

Nestled somewhere between a field of daffodils and sidewalk chalk memories you fulfill the dreams I had as a child.

Then,

now,

tomorrow,

always,

it's you.

I was once a single flower — *his* daffodil. Now, I am a meadow full of flowers I planted *myself.*

The Flower

I've slept inside of you. Finding comfort in your familiarity. Now, I must wake up and burn my skin in the daylight.

Acknowledgments

A tremendous thank you to the fiercely talented team of women who helped bring my vision to life. Chelsea Davis, my editor, thank you for believing in my words. Tree Abraham, my designer, your patience and attention to detail shines through every page of this book. A long sought-after dream came true because of each of you. Thank you for your time, patience, and devotion to making it a reality.

To my extended family, the Abramson-Greener clan, I am a better person for knowing you. I love you all dearly and I'm thankful to have you in my corner.

To my brother and sister, thank you for encouraging me to share my words and parts of our story. It has been a great comfort and relief having you by my side from the very beginning.

My father, my protector, my sword, there is no love greater than the one I have for you. Thank you for allowing me to use your strength on days I couldn't harbor my own.

My lover, my muse, if this book wasn't enough to prove it, I love and admire you profoundly. Through it all, you stood by me. Thank you for your loyalty and love. Thank you for always being there.

And to the woman, without whom I would not be here today, my mother, I love you.

To my little darlings, my readers, thank you for your support and kindness. Thank you for taking an interest in me and finding my words worthwhile of a purchase. Your support means everything to me.

Lastly, to the little girl inside of me desperately needing to be heard and recognized, we did it. After all these years, through the tears, the doubts, and fears, we did it. I hope you have finally found your freedom, little one.

About The Author

Encouraged by her own experiences and fantasies, Brittany Priore started writing at 14-years-old as a way to cope with her parents' divorce and the repercussions that shortly followed – anxiety, panic, and agoraphobia. Writing became a form of therapy. It created an outlet that allowed her to cope with the hardships she was facing at a young age. An age that can embody isolation and insecurity which can warp a young mind into believing such feelings are unique to their own being. Eventually, Brittany's creative outlet evolved from dear diary entries into more structured poetry and prose. She carved her thoughts and feelings into written words and set off on a journey to share her experiences with others in hopes that they, too, can find strength in them.

Made in the USA
Columbia, SC
08 December 2020